CUP FEVER

ROB CHILDS

COUNTY CUP

Book Six
SEMI-FINAL STAGE

West v North

Cup Fever

Illustrated by Robin Lawrie

CORGI YEARLING BOOKS

COUNTY CUP 6 : CUP FEVER
A CORGI YEARLING BOOK : 0 440 863880

First publication in Great Britain

PRINTING HISTORY
Corgi Yearling edition published 2000

1 3 5 7 9 10 8 6 4 2

Set in 12/15 pt New Century Schoolbook by
Phoenix Typesetting, Ilkley, West Yorkshire

Corgi Yearling Books are published by Transworld Publishers,
61–63 Uxbridge Road, Ealing, London W5 5SA,
a division of The Random House Group Ltd,
in Australia by Random House Australia (Pty) Ltd,
20 Alfred Street, Milsons Point, Sydney, NSW 2061, Australia,
in New Zealand by Random House New Zealand Ltd,
18 Poland Road, Glenfield, Auckland 10, New Zealand
and in South Africa by Random House (Pty) Ltd,
Endulini, 5a Jubilee Road, Parktown 2193, South Africa.

Made and printed in Great Britain by
Cox & Wyman Ltd, Reading, Berkshire